How to Make a Kite

Written by Paul Reeder
Illustrated by Manu Smith

To: paul@xcelent.com.usa
From: karauna@xcelent.com.cook

Hi Paul - do you remember how I told you that when I was a little boy, I lived on an island called Aitutaki? Aitutaki is in the Cook Islands. We didn't have a television, so we had to think of other things to do.

Today I found some old photos. They made me think of one day a long time ago, when I was playing with my friends Teina, Tunui, Ripeta, and Merito.

Merito showed us all a new book about kites her grandmother had sent her for her birthday.

When we sat down to look at the book, we saw most of the kites looked very hard to make.

Ripeta found one that looked easier to make, and I said to the others we should all make a kite and see whose kite would fly the highest.

The book told us the materials we would need. The book said…

You will need:

- string
- thick paper or plastic
- two strong bamboo sticks, 2 feet (60 cm) long
- one strong bamboo stick, 5 inches (13 cm) long
- sticky tape
- paint for decoration.

Tunui said we could go and get some string from his auntie. I told them about all the plastic at the airport where my dad worked. I said I thought they might let us use some of that.

Ripeta told us they had some bamboo growing by their house. She said her big sister might cut down some bamboo for us to use.

Teina said he had lots of paint and sticky tape at his house, and we could make our kites there.

We saw Ripeta's big sister walking along the beach. We called out to her and told her we were going to make some kites. She said she would come with us and help make the kites.

We all ran home and told our parents where we were going, and what we were going to do.

Plastic

First we went to the airport to see if we could have some plastic. Dad asked why we wanted it.

When I told him it was to make some kites, he said that sounded like fun. He gave us lots of plastic.

Ripeta's house was close to the airport, so we went there next. Ripeta's sister took a long saw and cut enough bamboo branches for us to use.

Our next stop was Tunui's auntie's house to collect the string we would need.

Then, with our arms full of plastic, bamboo, and string, we made our way to Teina's house.

Teina's dad put the paint and sticky tape out on the grass so we could work outside. We all put the rest of the things down.

Teina said we should look at the book again, to see what we should do now that we had all the things we needed to make our kites.

We all sat down on the grass while Merito read the instructions from her book.

The book told us what to do and had pictures to help us make the kite. The book said…

How to make your kite

- Cut one bamboo stick to 2 feet (60 cm) long.

- Cut the other stick to 18 inches (45 cm) long.

- Tie the short bamboo stick to the long stick just above halfway. They will make a cross shape.

- Tie some string around all four ends of the bamboo sticks. This will make a diamond shape.

- Place the four bamboo sticks onto a large sheet of plastic.

- Cut the plastic out, leaving it 2 inches (6 cm) wider than the diamond shape.

- Fold the extra 2 inches (6 cm) over the top of the string and stick it to the plastic.

- Cut 10 feet (3 m) of string. Tie one end to where the bamboo sticks cross, tie the other end to the short stick and wind it around the short stick.

- Cut three strips of plastic, 3 feet (90 cm) long. Stick them to the bottom of the kite to make a tail.

- Paint the kite and the tail.

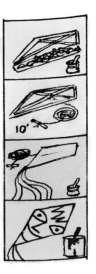

Tunui said that we should start at the beginning and follow the steps as we went along.

We all worked very hard. Ripeta's sister was a big help. She was good at making kites. All the kites looked really great when they were finished. They were all the same shape but they were painted with different shades and patterns.

While we waited for the paint to dry, Teina's mother came out with something for us to eat and drink. We were all feeling very happy when we carried our kites back down to the beach.

Merito said she thought her kite would fly the highest.
I said I thought mine would be the fastest kite.

Ripeta's sister just laughed and said we would see
who was right when we got to the beach.

When we got to the beach we looked at the book
again to see how to make our kites fly.

The book told us what to do. The book said…

How to Fly Your Kite

- Hold the string in one hand and the kite in your other hand.

- Stand with your back to the wind..

- Begin to run.

- Let go of the kite as you run but hold on tight to the string and your kite will fly up into the sky.

We all found a place on the beach where we wouldn't run into each other. Then we set off with our backs to the wind, running along the sand. We ran as fast as we could and the kites all flew into the sky. I looked up and saw my kite flying high in the sky. I felt very happy, and as I looked around, I could see all my friends felt happy too.

Did you ever fly a kite Paul? Tell me what you did when you were a boy in your next e-mail.

Good-bye for now,

Karauna

Index